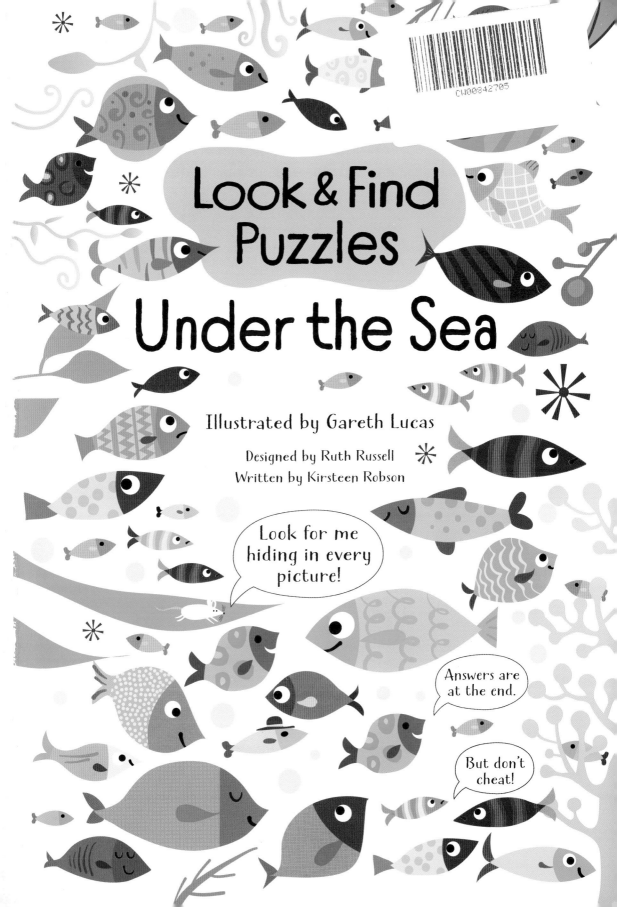

Spot a little blue crab.

Can you see a watch?

Can you find... 3 pink shells like this   another toy diver

2

Who's wearing a hat?

2 other spotted fish

2 star earrings like this

3 more purple shells

3

Find three more flying fish like me.

Can you find...

6 more gulls

2 other red oars

4

another one
of these

3 more groups
of bright fish

another
rubber ring

Who's got a bowl of noodles?

Which octopus has green eyes?

Can you find...

another paper hat

5 more gold bracelets

Spot an octopus wearing socks.

6 other starfish

another 2 of these

3 octopuses just like this

Who has a
spotted beak?

Can you find...   2 more blue   5 other
                        buckets   dominoes

8

Find a fish with a sparkly tiara on her head.

3 more of these

another golden cup

1 more fish like this

Who's wearing a life jacket?

Can you find...   another purple submarine   3 more bananas

a shoe that
matches this one

2 more blue
bags

14

another fish
like this

1 more
red shoe

2 other
yellow balls

15

3 other
carrots

a fish just
like this

another
compass

Spot a fish with a pirate's eye patch.

Can you see a swimming parrot?

Can you find...

3 more pirates' hats

2 other seahorses just like this

18

Find an old knife, fork and spoon.

another black flag

3 more starfish

2 other barrels

Who's wearing sunglasses?

Can you find... 3 more goldfish

another 3 of these

21

2 more toothbrushes

3 blue flags like this

1 other tube of toothpaste

Find two fish that match.

Where's my basket?

Can you find...

2 more blue shells

a shell that matches this

Which two seahorses are linking tails?

Spot three little orange fish.

Can you find...   2 more ponies   another jellyfish, just the same

Help me find a yellow fish.

Can you find... a snow shovel like this another 3 balls

24

Can you find...   2 more parrots   another 3 tomatoes

a matching
guitar

3 other
palm trees

2 fish like
this one

Can you find...

1 other
watering can

1 more pink
sunhat

2 bags the
same as this

3 more
pufferfish

another one
of these

Answers

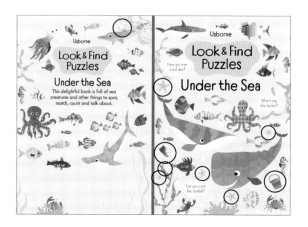

Cover

2–3

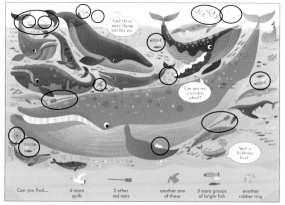

4–5

6–7

8–9

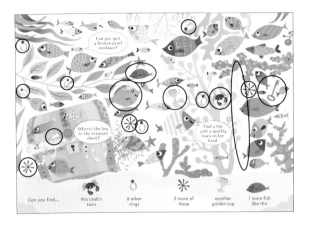

10–11

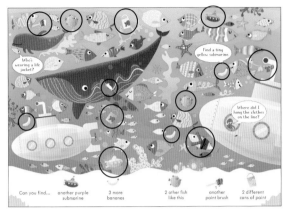

12–13

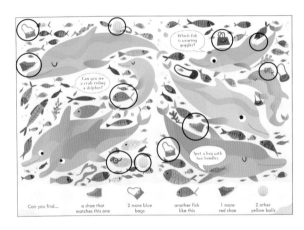

14–15

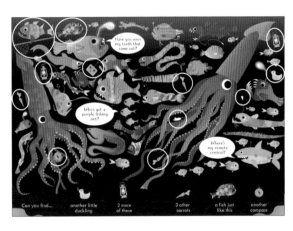

16–17

18–19

20–21

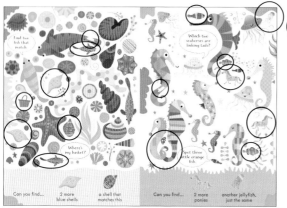

22-23

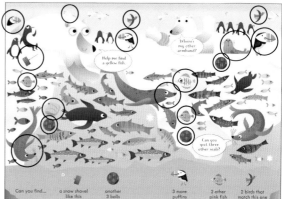

24-25

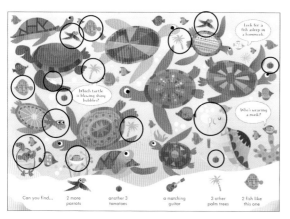

26-27

28-29